Yakkinn the Swamp Tortoi

Book One

THE MOST DANGEROUS YEAR

By

Guundie and Gerald Kuchling

Era

Summer is over, and the hot days are gone. Bushes, shrubs and trees are parched, the grass is brown and everything waits for rain. It has been dry for half a year.

When the first chilly nights arrive in the bushland, something happens in an underground nest. Last spring, a Tortoise mother carefully prepared the nest for her five eggs. After closing and concealing the hole her duties were ended and she left.

Now it is autumn, the Tortoise eggs are fully developed and ready to hatch.

Spring   Summer   Autumn

The Tortoise babies push their noses against the egg shells. Yakkinn kicks and struggles hardest and her egg is the first to crack open. Three other eggs crack too, but in one egg, there is no movement. It was not buried deep enough, warmed up too much during the hottest days of summer and did not survive.

After Yakkinn and her three Tortoise siblings hatch out, they start to breathe. There is just enough air for them in the nest, but there is no light so they don't see. And they cannot leave because the dry clay is too hard. The Tortoise hatchlings sit still and wait.

When the first heavy winter rains come pounding down, the water soaks into the ground. The hard clay becomes soft and the Tortoises get ready to leave their nest.

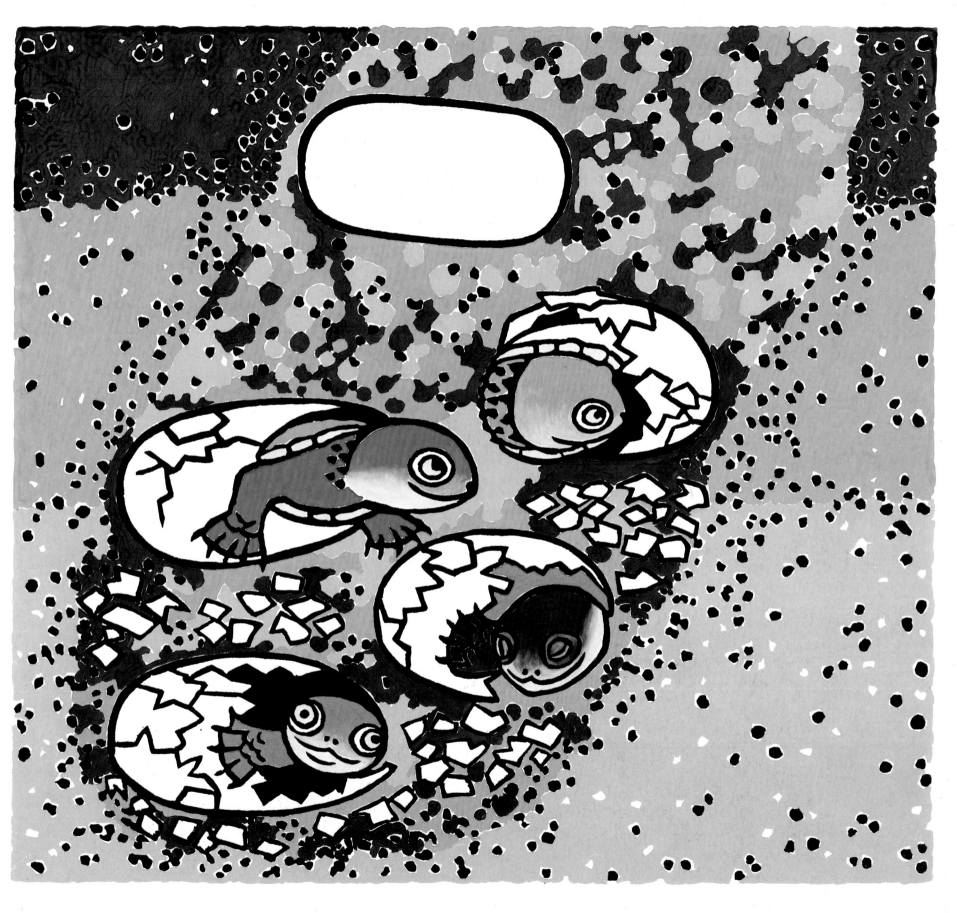

Yakkinn, the biggest and strongest, goes first. Digging with all four legs, she slowly pushes her way up through the soil. She makes it easier for the others who follow her trail.

One hatchling after another emerges from the nest. The four short-necked Western Australian Swamp Tortoises come out of the ground. Each one weighs about five grams, like a cherry, less than a quarter of an ounce.

It is raining. The hatchlings get a first drink. Their skin, eyes and shell are moistened and their lungs fill with fresh air.

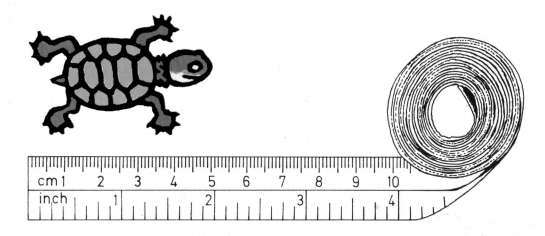

Yakkinn starts off the journey and the other Tortoises stay close by. Together they climb over lumps of clay and through leaves. Crossing cracks in the ground and struggling among branches and roots, they find a tiny puddle, deep enough to slip into and have a good rest.

On the next sunny day, the puddle dries up. The hatchlings hide under leaf litter where it is cool and moist. Again, they sit still and wait, head and feet tightly tucked under their shells.

The winter rains continue. After a few days of heavy rain, water floods around the trees and shrubs. Clay pans, troughs and hollows in the soil become pools. The bushland turns into a swamp.

Plants grow, seeds sprout, trees and shrubs become green, frogs start calling.

Yakkinn and the other three Swamp Tortoises leave their hide-out and move into a pool.

Once they learn to surface for breathing, they practise diving and swimming in deep water. They find out how to warm up in the shallows and how to bask on the shore or on little islands. At any scary sound or movement, the Tortoises jump back and hide under water. They can hold their breath for a quarter of an hour.

Most of the time Yakkinn and the others look for food. They quickly learn to catch the tiny water creatures that appear everywhere in the pools. Larvae of dragonflies and mosquitoes develop. Tadpoles grow from the eggs laid by frogs a few days earlier.

Fairy shrimp and water fleas hatch from eggs that have been resting in the dry soil for many months. Worms, which have spent the summer tightly coiled up in the ground, wake from their sleep. Boatmen, water beetles and backswimmers fly into the swamp.

The baby Tortoises are hungry and eat a lot.

Other swamp animals are hungry too, and some of them can eat little Tortoises. Yakkinn and her siblings are cautious and alert, but sometimes that is not enough.

One of the hatchlings is paddling, unaware that a Heron has come into the pool, looking for fish and frogs. The Heron discovers the little Tortoise, strikes quickly and gobbles it up. This is sad, but nature must make sure that all creatures can eat.

Another hatchling is picked up by a duck. It is lucky and escapes being eaten, though it has bite marks on its shell. The duck has to look for something else.

Three little Tortoises are left and now they are more careful. They quickly hide when a Tiger Snake slips into their pool to take a bath.

Another time, Yakkinn is basking alone on the shore, but she remains alert and soon senses danger. Sure enough, a Black-tailed Monitor has spotted her.

With a big snap, the monitor goes for Yakkinn, but she dives straight into deep water and escapes.

With many rainy days, and some sunshine in between, winter passes. As the days get warmer, the three baby Tortoises eat more and grow faster.

Birds often visit the swamp. Red-capped Parrots and Ring-necked Parrots, Crested Pigeons and Galahs land on the shores. They drink, bathe, chat and eat plants or seeds.

When an adult Swamp Tortoise visits the hatchling pool, the little ones have a close look and circle around. Yakkinn sniffs curiously. The grown-up soon moves on again.

Spring arrives and wildflowers appear everywhere. Trees and shrubs are blooming. The heavy rains have stopped and water becomes scarce.

Thirsty visitors turn up at the hatchling pool - Bluetongue Lizards, Bearded Dragons, Shinglebacks and Legless Lizards. Bandicoots, Kangaroos and Echidnas also come to drink.

Another guest, a Long-necked Tortoise, is passing through the swamp. Long-necks live elsewhere - they prefer pools that have water all year round and never dry up.

The spring days grow warmer and warmer and the pools shrink until only puddles are left. Plenty of tiny water creatures crowd together in the last puddles.

The Swamp Tortoises eat as much as possible. They need to be strong because soon water and food will disappear. Now the hatchlings weigh five times more than when they left the nest. Yakkinn is still the strongest and heaviest.

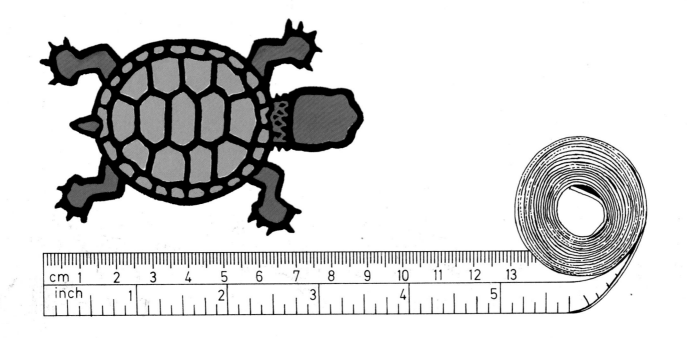

Late spring is the time of the year when the swamp dries up. The puddles are finally empty. Without water, the Swamp Tortoises must look for a hiding place and they take refuge in a pile of leaves. But soon this hide-out heats up.

Yakkinn pushes under the leaves. She finds a tunnel leading down into the soil and buries herself as deeply as she can. The second Tortoise hides in a crack in the ground nearby.

The third Tortoise walks off. It leaves the protective bush cover and crawls into the open, over the hot, dry clay. From the sky, a Raven dives down, snatches the hatchling up and takes it away.

Summer comes with hot days and months of drought.

Two Tortoise hatchlings are still alive. One of them sleeps in the crack, but this is not deep enough below the ground and does not protect against the heat of summer. During the hottest time the hatchling dries up and dies.

The last of the four Tortoises, Yakkinn, is buried safely in the tunnel. The heat cannot get down into her shelter and it remains cool and even a bit damp.

Throughout summer, Yakkinn stays fast asleep.

In autumn, the chilly nights return to the bushland. After sleeping for half a year, Yakkinn wakes up.

When the rains begin she leaves her underground shelter and finds herself a pool. During winter and spring, she will swim, dive, bask, eat and grow. In summer, she will go underground again.

Now, Yakkinn the Swamp Tortoise begins her second year. She has survived the first, the most dangerous year in her life.

Summer      Autumn

Winter   Spring

WESTERN SWAMP TORTOISE

Pseudemydura umbrina

In Australia there is no land-dwelling herbivorous tortoise. Australians call freshwater chelonians 'tortoises', although in other countries they are called 'turtles' or 'terrapins'. The local Aboriginals, the Nyungar, call them 'Yakkinn'. The Western Swamp Tortoise is the smallest Australian freshwater tortoise (adults weigh 250-550 grams). They are only found in the south-western corner of Western Australia, in seasonal swamps on clay soils of the Swan River Valley near Perth.

The first Western Swamp Tortoise known to science was acquired by the Museum of Natural History in Vienna, Austria, in 1839. It was not until 1953 that two further specimens were found in a swamp near Perth. This rediscovery generated much public and scientific interest and concern regarding the con-servation of the rare animal.

The Western Swamp Tortoise was studied by Andrew Burbidge during the 1960s and 1970s and, since 1988, by Gerald Kuchling. Its biology is unique and relies on a sequence of events in its habitat. During winter and spring, the tortoises are active in the shallow waters and feed on live food. During the dry summer months, they lie dormant in naturally occurring holes or under leaf litter.

In late spring, when the swamps dry out, the females lay three to five eggs in an underground nest. Harsh summer conditions take their toll on eggs. From surviving eggs, hatchlings emerge the following autumn with a body mass of three to six grams. The hatchlings must grow to about twenty grams in their first winter and spring in order to have a chance of surviving the summer. They only grow enough if the rainfall is good in winter and spring. A high percentage of hatchlings don't make it beyond their first summer. Western Swamp Tortoises take ten to twenty years to mature and have a life span similar to humans. Even females with an age of fifty to sixty years lay eggs. This long reproductive life of individuals balances the heavy loss of eggs and hatchlings.

Some native animals predate tortoise eggs and hatchlings. No native predator can harm adult Swamp Tortoises, because they have a hard, protective shell. However, the introduced European Red Fox, dogs and cats take a heavy toll of tortoises in Australia,including adult Western Swamp Tortoises.

Conservation

Most Western Swamp Tortoise habitat has been lost. Almost all the area that they would have occupied 200 years ago has been cleared and drained for agriculture or developed for housing and industry. As well, clay from some tortoise swamps has been mined for brick and tile manufacture. Two small remaining areas of habitat were declared as nature reserves in 1962, but tortoise numbers in the reserves dropped from about 200 in the 1960s to less than 30 by 1987. By 1985, the species had all but disappeared from one of the nature reserves. The main causes for this decline were drought and predation by introduced foxes.

A captive colony of 25 Western Swamp Tortoises was founded in 1959. However, despite some breeding during the 1960s and 1970s, there was no reproduction between 1980 and 1987. By 1987 only 17 remained in captivity. The Western Swamp Tortoise, Australia's most endangered animal, was on the brink of extinction. With about fifty individuals left it became the rarest tortoise or turtle on earth.

In 1988, Gerald Kuchling started a rescue operation for the Western Swamp Tortoise. He established a very successful captive breeding project with funding and support from the Western Australian Department of Conservation and Land Management, the World Wide Fund for Nature (WWF) Australia, Perth Zoo, the Australian Nature Conservation Agency and the University of Western Australia. The Western Swamp Tortoise Recovery Team was founded in 1990. It has prepared and published a detailed Recovery Plan and tries to raise funds for its implementation.

Since 1988, the reproduction and ecology of the last wild population of Swamp Tortoises has been studied intensively. Fox-proof fences have been constructed around the two nature reserves, areas of former habitat have been purchased by the Western Australian Government and added to the nature reserves. In dry winters, swamps in one reserve are supplemented by ground water.

The recovery actions for the Western Swamp Tortoise are supported worldwide by organisations, businesses and individuals. In addition to the organisations mentioned above, sponsors include the Bunesverband fur fachgerechten Natur- und Artenschutz (Germany), the British Chelonia Group, the AG Schildkroten und Panzerechsen (DGHT, Germany), the California Turtle and Tortoise Club, the Western Australian Water Authority, the IUCN Tortoise and Freshwater Turtle Specialist Group, East-West Veterinary Supplies, Aherns and other companies and individuals too numerous to mention. With these efforts, the number of Western Swamp Tortoises has increased to over 150 in just seven years, although the number of breeding adults is still critically low.

The re-introduction of captive bred Western Swamp Tortoises into the wild started in 1994. Every purchase of this book contributes to the ongoing conservation programme.

GUUNDIE KUCHLING was born in Salzburg, Austria. She graduated as Master of Fine Arts at the Academy of Applied Arts in Vienna in 1980. Besides setting up an organic farm in the southern part of Austria, she worked as a painter, sculptor and printmaker and taught arts and crafts in high schools. In 1985, Guundie and Gerald joined their interests and lives. Since then, Guundie cooperates in Gerald's tortoise and turtle conservation programmes in Madagascar and Australia; her art work is widely exhibited and represented in many collections. Her first book Today is a Day was published by Cygnet Books.

GERALD KUCHLING was born in Vienna, Austria. Since his early childhood, he has been interested, and cared for, tortoises and turtles. He studied biology and was employed at the Natural History Museum in Vienna. After receiving his PhD at the University of Vienna in 1979, Gerald worked as a postdoctoral fellow at the University of Gottingen, Germany. Research, field surveys and conservation work with tortoises and turtles has taken him to Yugoslavia, Madagascar, Australia and China. Since 1987, Gerald has worked as a Research Fellow at the University of Western Australia. He is Principal Investigator of the Western Swamp Tortoise Recovery Team.

First published and designed in 1995
by Chelonia Enterprises

This edition published 1996 by ERA PUBLICATIONS
220 Grange Road, Flinders Park, SA 5025 Australia

Text & illustration © Guundie and Gerald Kuchling, 1995

**National Library of Australia
Cataloguing-in-Publication Data:**
Kuchling, Guundie.
    Yakkinn the swamp tortoise: the most dangerous year.

    ISBN 1 86374 272 7.

    1. Turtles - Western Australia - Juvenile literature.
    I. Kuchling, Gerald. II Title. III. Title: Most dangerous
    year.

597.92

Available in:

Australia from Era Publications, 220 Grange Road,
Flinders Park, South Australia 5025

Canada from Vanwell Publishing Ltd, 1 Northrup Cresc.,
PO Box 2131, Stn B, St Catharines, ONT L2M 6P5

New Zealand from Reed Publishing (NZ) Ltd,
39 Rawene Road, Birkenhead, Auckland 10

Singapore, Malaysia & Brunei from Publishers Marketing
Services Pte Ltd, 10-C Jalan Ampas, #07-01 Ho Seng Lee
Flatted Warehouse, Singapore 1232

United Kingdom from Heinemann Educational Publishers,
Halley Court, Jordan Hill, Oxford OX2 8EJ

The original artwork for *Yakkinn the Swamp Tortoise* is linocuts which are available in limited edition prints.

Yakkinn is an Aboriginal (Nyungar) word for tortoise. Dumbartung Aboriginal Artists' Advisory Committee approved its use for this book.